THE 4TH STEP
Examining Your Survival Skills

Made a searching and fearless moral inventory of ourselves.

Carla Wills-Brandon, M.A.

Health Communications, Inc.
Deerfield Beach, Florida

Carla Wills-Brandon
Houston, Texas

©1991 Carla Wills-Brandon
ISBN 1-55874-181-X

Publisher: Health Communications, Inc.
3201 S.W. 15th Street
Deerfield Beach, Florida 33442-8190

DEDICATION

This book is dedicated to those who were here before me and from whom I have learned a great deal about life

My Grandparents, Ted and Bertha Wills
My In-laws, Sylvan and Elizabeth Brandon
My Aunt, Naomi Warren
My Great-Aunt and Uncle, Ralph and Helen Walton
My Grandparents, Fred and Florence Smith

This book is also dedicated to the
memory of Ira and Norman, both
of whom gave of themselves
unconditionally. They now live
with the stars but in spirit
they live with us all.

CONTENTS

ACKNOWLEDGMENTS

My books are never a solo project. I love to write and am able to do so because of the tolerance, love, support and assistance I receive from so many. I need to thank my husband Michael for listening to my numerous rewrites late into the night. If it were not for his patience, I doubt this work would be as readable as it is today. To my son Aaron I say, "Yes, Momma gets a little wacky when she writes, and I am sorry. I love you." To my friend and the editor of this work, Marie Stilkind, "We did it again!" Thanks for making my work shine. To my running buddies in this business, Robert Becker, Bryan Robinson, Joy Miller and Ruth Fishel: "We are the killer bees!" Thanks for your support. And finally, I would like to express my gratitude and immense appreciation for the divine genius of Dr. Bob and Bill W., the founders of the 12 Steps and the 12-Step movement. My spirituality assures me that, though they were only here for a brief moment, their gift of recovery will last forever.

HOW TO USE THIS 4TH-STEP WORKBOOK ON YOUR OWN OR IN A GROUP

For most, the thought of doing one's first 4th Step is an overwhelming prospect. Some people become so overwhelmed with the idea that they procrastinate indefinitely. Many find that the only way they can focus themselves mentally to complete this step is by turning off the telephone, locking the doors, unplugging the radio or television and, with pen in hand, begin to write. For them, solitude and time alone allow the feelings and memories to emerge. If this is your path in working this step, know you have my support.

Others become so overwhelmed with their feelings and memories they put their 4th Step aside in order to seek relief from the emotions it stirs up. For these individuals it is sometimes useful to complete this workbook in a support group. Support groups can provide the safety and security which is so necessary for many of us when we are dredging up the past and exploring our difficulties in the present. The fellowship of a support group allows for dispersion of the fear many feel about examining their unresolved pain.

If your support group chooses to use this 4th-Step workbook as an aid to the recovery process, it is useful to follow a few guidelines. In working the 4th Step, it is sometimes necessary to process feelings as they surface, rather than waiting until the step is completed. Because of this need to talk about feelings while the book is being worked on, I suggest you break down part of this workbook into four sections. These sections, which are chapter heads, are easy to identify.

1. The Early Years.
2. The Learning Years
3. The Exploring Years
4. More Growing Years

The support group using this format could allow two weeks or two meeting sessions for discussion time of each section. Ideally the support group should be a closed meeting consisting of no more than 10 participants. In some situations the above guidelines will not suit the support group, so set up guidelines which will benefit the recovery of all involved. Remember, the most important ingredient in a successful support group is an element of safety. If the group does not feel secure, sharing becomes difficult.

The 4th Step is the first of the active action steps within the 12-Step recovery process. It allows us an opportunity to squarely face who we are, what we are made up of, our survival skills, our old grief and anger and where we come from. If you are apprehensive about beginning this 4th Step, know first that this is *normal*. Secondly, take comfort in knowing that after all has been written down on paper, you will probably ask yourself, "Why did I fear this step so much?"

I hope most of you will feel a sense of accomplishment when this 4th Step is completed. You will understand yourself a little bit better and you will feel as though you have some direction in your recovery. You will be able to embrace all of your feelings, knowing they are not the enemy but necessary for your healing. This workbook is not an end but a beginning for self-discovery and continued growth.

Take care of yourselves, and may your own sense of spirituality guide you on your path of recovery.

Carla Wills-Brandon

CHAPTER

1

A Beginning

When I was growing up in my own dysfunctional family of origin, I developed a specific set of survival skills which were tailored for me by my own creative child mind. These survival skills were wonderful and enabled my survival in a family which was experiencing overwhelming pain, trauma, anger, addiction and chaos.

With these childhood tools, I was able to live in my family believing everything happening around me was *normal*. These dysfunctional skills worked well within my family system, but when I left home and began applying them to the world in general, they backfired on me.

I could not understand why those creative behaviors I had developed in childhood, which had worked for so long, were now only creating pain. Even the addictions I had developed, which initially blunted out the stark realities of life, no longer gave me the feeling of security they had once provided. It was as if there wasn't anywhere to hide. Booze, pills, food, cigarettes, sex, work, compulsive spending and even trashy love novels no longer seemed to work.

In my family of origin it had been very important to always give to others and never refuse the requests of anyone in need. By always giving, I received the approval I so desperately craved. If I did not refuse anyone with the word *no*, I didn't have to experience rejection, anger or abandonment. Unfortunately, always giving, giving, giving in adulthood began to really *hurt*. It cost me not only my savings account, a vacuum cleaner, a set of Corningware, a dinette set and more, but also my self-respect. I started to feel really used and abused by so-called friends and I also felt abandoned.

Never saying *no* forced me into situations which were unsafe. It also set me up to attract "takers," who kept me in the role of "victim." Many in recovery today would refer to the above as "defects of character." This phrase originated as a tool for describing those behaviors which are a consequence of alcoholic drinking.

The phrase "defects of character" has been used for over 50 years by members of the support group for recovering alcoholics called *Alcoholics Anonymous*. All of the above may be "defects of character," but I believe many of these "defects" are also survival skills which were learned in childhood and which ran amok in adulthood.

Aside from my dysfunctional behavior, I also view my addictions as survival skills. Addiction provided for me a sense of predictability in my unpredictable family of origin. Life in my family could be very chaotic, and in response my emotions would overwhelm me. When I used food, co-dependent caretaking and eventually alcohol or drugs to cover up my feelings, my emotions leveled out. I could always predict how I would feel if I ate too much or drank to excess, and this predictability of emotion brought for me a sense of security.

My addictions allowed me to survive the trauma of my younger years. The behaviors associated with these addictions provided for me a pair of rose-colored glasses which filtered out the realities of the world I lived in. Viewing my world while protected by a false sense of security allowed me to appear quite functional.

Eventually though, the wall of safety which my dysfunctional survival skills had provided for so long came crumbling down around me. I was left frightened, alone and more vulnerable than ever before. There wasn't any bottle of booze to hide in, pill to escape with or bag of potato chips to lose myself in. Giving, giving, giving to others now only brought pain, and never saying no left me feeling victimized. Angry people terrified me, and I was afraid if I told those around me how I really felt about them, I would be abandoned, doomed to live alone forever.

God scared me and I didn't know who I was or what I wanted to be now that I was grown up. My life felt hopeless and overwhelming. I was an adult woman, living in an adult world, frightened without the rose-colored glasses of addiction and dysfunction which had protected me from the realities of life for so long.

For over 50 years Alcoholics Anonymous (AA) has been the most successful vehicle for those suffering from the disease of alcoholism to achieve sobriety. Today the 12 Steps for achieving sobriety from alcoholic drinking, initially developed by Dr. Bob, an alcoholic physician, and Bill W., a stockbroker who had also suffered from the disease of excessive drink, are not only used by recovering alcoholics. The Steps, which have become guides for healthy living for millions of otherwise hopeless alcoholics, have also been used by those suffering from other addictions.

Those addicted to drugs, pills, food, sex, work, money, spending, emotions, love, people, cigarettes and more have found relief, answers and security with the aid of the 12 Steps of Alcoholics Anonymous. The original 12 Steps, as presented in the Big Book, the Alcoholics Anonymous guide to successful recovery from alcoholism, are as follows:

The 12 Steps Of Alcoholics Anonymous

1. We admitted we were powerless over alcohol — that our lives had become unmanageable.

2. Came to believe that a Power greater than ourselves could restore us to sanity.
3. Made a decision to turn our will and our lives over to the care of God *as we understood Him.*
4. Made a searching and fearless moral inventory of ourselves.
5. Admitted to God, to ourselves and to another human being the exact nature of our wrongs.
6. Were entirely ready to have God remove all our defects of character.
7. Humbly asked Him to remove our shortcomings.
8. Made a list of all persons we had harmed and became willing to make amends to them all.
9. Made direct amends to such people whenever possible, except when to do so would injure them or others.
10. Continued to take personal inventory and when we were wrong promptly admitted it.
11. Sought through prayer and meditation to improve our conscious contact with God, *as we understood Him,* praying only for knowledge of His will for us and the power to carry that out.*
12. Having had a spiritual awakening as the result of these steps, we tried to carry this message to alcoholics, and to practice these principles in all our affairs.

Support groups like Narcotics Anonymous, Adult Children of Alcoholics Anonymous and Sexaholics Anonymous have patterned themselves after Alcoholics Anonymous with the 12 Steps serving as the backbone of each group. The basic format of the 12 Steps is used, changing only what one is addicted to (i.e., work, spending, food, emotions) and at times the gender of the Higher Power (i.e., Her, It).

As a consequence of the success of these Steps, there are numerous 12-Step support groups all around the world. One need only look in the yellow pages of the telephone book when traveling in the States or even abroad to realize how popular these support groups are today. For many seeking answers to recovery from addiction and dysfunctional behavior, these support groups provide

---

*Some 12-Step groups have changed the gender of God or Higher Power to read as follows: ". . . conscious contact with God as we understood God, praying only for knowledge of God's will for us and the power to carry that out."

step-by-step problem-solving techniques for those who have previously had only their dysfunctional survival skills to rely on.

Not only are present problems solved in healthy ways, but past traumas can finally be resolved and self-respect rebuilt. The 12 Steps are a healthy alternative to the dysfunctional survival skills learned in childhood. Many of us did not receive the skills and tools necessary for healthy living. As a consequence, we feel inadequate in confronting the changes and challenges which are a part of the life experience.

Since our old survival skills protected us from life's problems, many of us are grasping for healthy tools when confronted with the difficulties of life today or the unresolved trauma of yesterday. Without the old skills to hide behind, the search for alternatives can seem hopeless. Fortunately, the 12 Steps provide the healthy tools necessary for replacing those survival skills which no longer work.

Over the last decade, the Adult Children of Alcoholics movement has swelled to an all-time high in membership. These 12-Step support groups have provided many with the answers necessary for healing to begin. Unfortunately, this movement has not yet attained the wisdom that Alcoholics Anonymous has achieved over many, many years. This statement is not intended to discredit the ACoA movement. If one researches the history of AA, it will clearly show there were many initial difficulties. Many recovering alcoholics within the initial development of Alcoholics Anonymous went out and drank in response to the internal problems experienced by the movement.

If an Adult Child of an Alcoholic comes to my office seeking assistance, I will tell them they must attend ACoA support group meetings before I can agree to work with them. Some of the responses I receive are as follows:

- All I need is therapy.
- I hate crowds.
- What if my family finds out?
- I don't have time.
- I've been before and it didn't feel as though people in the group were progressing. They seemed stuck in the problem.

The first four excuses can usually be addressed and resolved fairly quickly, but the fifth is a bit more difficult to resolve. It is difficult to debate because for the most part it is a correct perception of a *particular* ACoA group. On top of this, recovering alcoholics who have experienced years of stability in AA will share with me some of the following when unsatisfied with an ACoA group:

- The group is into sitting in pain.
- There seems to be a lot of blame.
- I never heard about the solution.
- They didn't talk about the Steps.

Most ACoAs initially are in a great deal of pain and need to experience their pain about growing up with alcoholism. Most of us fear emotional pain and initially have difficulty being around somebody else who is experiencing these feelings.

By being around another in distress, our own unresolved pain moves from deep within to the surface and begins to make its presence known to us. "Out of sight, out of mind" has been a family motto for most of us. To hear another in pain confronts us with our own unresolved feelings of sadness, anger, loneliness and shame.

Adult Children of Alcoholics in early recovery appear to friends, family and peers to be blaming others for their own personal difficulties. Because of this, the ACoA movement in general continues to receive a great deal of criticism from outsiders. To the newcomer to ACoA who does not understand the recovery process, this can be very unsettling. Responses from newcomers and those outside the ACoA movement usually are, "All these ACoAs do is complain and gripe," or "What is wrong with these people? All they want to do is dig up the past! What good can that possibly do? Look how they are hurting their families by talking about this stuff! Why can't they just live and let live?"

Adult Children of Alcoholics come from family systems where it was never acceptable to talk about what was really going on around them while growing up. The belief that "If we don't talk about *it* and just ignore *it*, *it* will go away" is a strong one for most. It can initially feel very overwhelming to walk into a support group and hear people say:

- When my father was drunk, he . . .
- My mother would hit me when . . .
- I never felt loved by my parents because . . .
- As a child I felt alone, abandoned . . .
- When I was sexually abused . . .

We cannot begin to heal ourselves until we decide to talk about those things in childhood which produced resentment, painful feelings or confusion. When ACoAs begin talking about their past, (or debriefing, as some therapists refer to this process) it does sound like blaming and in most cases it is. As we begin talking about those things which were taboo for discussion during childhood, our feelings about those incidents begin to emerge.

Feelings like grief, rage, fear, abandonment and more begin to surface after years of imprisonment. These old locked-in unexpressed feelings are responsible for many of the emotional and physical problems we experience today. An example of this might be the hidden rage one carries about the alcoholic drunkenness a parent displayed in public which caused shame and embarrassment for the young son.

Today that young boy is a grown man who does not know how to express his rage, fearing he will lose control if he does. As a result of this belief system, his hidden rage manifests itself as migraine headaches, colitis, lower back pain or ulcers because he has never been able to talk about his feelings regarding the alcoholism in his family of origin.

By talking about his unresolved childhood trauma, he will begin to feel it, move through the rage and pain about these experiences and eventually heal from his past. No longer will his locked-in rage have to hit him in the lower back.

Another example of the unresolved past influencing the here and now might be the effects of unresolved grief a woman continues to carry about the death of her father 15 years ago on her current intimate relationships. As a consequence of the dysfunction in her family, this woman never learned how to express sadness and was never able to grieve the loss of her father.

As a result of this unexpressed grief, she hangs onto dysfunctional relationships for fear of experiencing loss. Many of her relationships are growth-stunting and even abusive, but she will not let go because she fears experiencing her aloneness. Her fear about being alone overwhelms her, and she panics at the thought of separating from these toxic relationships.

By talking about her father's death in ACoA meetings, working diligently through the old pain, she will not be as frightened at the thought of abandoning her dysfunctional relationships. Eventually she will move out of these relationships and into those which are based in health.

Most ACoAs do spend some time in blame after they discover their unresolved pain and resentment about growing up with addiction and family-of-origin dysfunction. Those adult children who allow themselves all their feelings of grief, rage and more eventually move out of blame. A healthy healing process moves one from blame into acceptance of what once was and understanding that the past no longer has the strong hold on the present that it used to. Admitting feelings like the following *allows the healing to begin.*

- I hated my mother's Valium addiction.
- I'm sad my childhood wasn't normal.
- I was so scared when my father drank.
- I'm angry with my parents.
- I have a lot of pain and rage about being whipped with the belt.
- I feel sad for the child that was me who was sexually abused.
- I hated all of the yelling in my family.
- Why couldn't my parents love me?

Unfortunately, some people do get stuck indefinitely in blaming their present-day difficulties on the past. They remain in the ACoA problem instead of moving toward healthy solutions. Healthy recovery involves taking responsibility for all of our feelings about our unresolved family-of-origin business and trauma, instead of denying it. Taking responsibility involves having all of our anger and grief about our past, while at the same time discovering how our present-day difficulties are repeated patterns of our dysfunctional past. With this information, we can begin resolving our own feelings about our childhood, then accept responsibility for our behavior in the here and now.

Some continue to blame their present-day behavior on the past, while at the same time not taking the steps necessary to resolve their feelings about past trauma. Unfortunately, these individuals are the ones who come to one support group after another, discussing the same issue or problem over and over again. Several years on down the line, they are still discussing the same issue at 12-Step meetings, because they have not discovered how to implement the 12 Steps into their lives.

Those who find themselves in one unhealthy relationship after another, but who do not address unresolved childhood emotional, physical or sexual abuse, are stuck in the recovery process. Using excuses like, "The past is the past. It's over and didn't really affect me," or "I just decided to forgive, live and let live," without experiencing the hidden feelings about these incidents is not acting responsibly. Taking responsibility for our unfinished family-of-origin business and trauma involves taking action. This leads us to our next discussion, which involves the 12 Steps in support groups.

Healthy ACoA 12-Step support groups will focus the majority of their discussion on how to apply the 12 Steps to the problems and difficulties ACoA's face in the here and now. Also, in mature ACoA meetings, discussion topics will involve the application of the 12 Steps to unresolved childhood pain. These meetings are not therapy, nor are the members supposed to offer counsel or therapeutic advice.

Fixing, counseling or caretaking within the support group is a blatant example of co-dependent behavior. These groups are *support* groups, and those who play junior counselor within ACoA meetings are in serious need of co-dependency therapy themselves.

A meeting which does not focus in on the 12 Steps (the solution), and instead only becomes an emotional dumping ground week after week (the problem), is not a healthy haven for successful healing. Unfortunately, because the ACoA movement is still fairly new it is inevitable that one will come across such meetings.

One client returned to my office complaining that the meeting he had been to had members promoting a local treatment center with evangelistic style during the group discussion. His concern about this was valid, and he never returned to this particular group. Fortunately for the ACoA movement, the majority of the support groups today promote healthy recovery, sharing only their "experience, strength and hope." These groups strongly suggest that their member use the 12 Steps to recover from those painful characteristics, behaviors and tendencies Adult Children of Alcoholics seem to have in common.

CHAPTER

2

*The Steps
Toward Healing*

1. We admitted we were powerless over alcohol, that our lives had become unmanageable.
2. Came to believe that a power greater than ourselves could restore us to sanity.
3. Made a decision to turn our will and lives over to the care of God *as we understood God.*

These first three Steps provide for ACoAs the words necessary to admit *defeat!*

This defeat or knowledge that one is tool-less, powerless, at a loss and unable to live life successfully in the adult world in healthy ways forces Adult Children of Alcoholics to admit "my life isn't working!" For so long, most of us have tried to make life work with the dysfunctional survival tool we developed in childhood, fearing our own confrontation with failure.

Few of us understand that our failure in adulthood is a consequence of our unhealthy survival skills from childhood. Acknowledging that our life in the here and now is not working as a result of our behaviors as adult children, is a huge step toward recovery. Also these first three Steps force AoCAs to admit, "I need *help!*"

Growing up with dysfunctions taught many of us that asking for help was a sign of weakness. Others of us did ask for help and, receiving none, learned that depending on anybody was pointless. By taking the first three steps, ACoAs can finally admit, "I can no longer do this thing called life by myself! I need help and am willing to ask for it." By doing this, adult children begin to acknowledge that their behavior isn't normal and that there must be a more successful way to live life.

Though the first three steps are very necessary for beginning the recovery process, the guts of the recovery process for all 12-Step programs seems to lie within the 4th Step.

Some time back my husband Michael and I were awakened by a burglar who had broken into our home. He walked into our bedroom, knowing there was someone occupying it, with intent to disarm our alarm and take whatever he could. When I saw him, he appeared quite intoxicated and beyond reasoning. He had an agenda and it was plain to see he planned to carry it out.

Fortunately Michael and I had resigned from Victims Anonymous some time earlier and we both managed to scare the intruder out of our house. A full alarm system didn't hurt and our own personal growth enabled both of us to think clearly and take the appropriate action necessary to secure our home. It was a frightening experience and we were angry with this violation, but were also able to heal from it.

By taking a good hard look at how our survival skills from childhood were keeping us in the role of "adult victim," we were able to learn how to take responsibility for ourselves in healthy ways.

For Michael, learning to reach out and ask for help enabled him to begin connecting with others who could be there to assist him, not feeling he had to handle all of life's problems by himself. His survival skills, which would wall him up from the world in order not to feel, had kept him in a great deal of isolation. This lifestyle also kept him trapped in the role of caretaker: always giving and never receiving.

Previous to exploring my own dysfunctional survival skills, I would not have reacted responsibly if confronted with an intruder in my home. I would have panicked and looked immediately toward Michael for solving the problem. My fear would have frozen me and I would have regressed to the small child who had been so violently abused in youth.

Michael, before examining his ineffective life skills, would have felt totally responsible for the situation. If the criminal had been successful, Michael would have felt like a failure, not acknowledging that I *too* had had a responsibility to react in adult ways. We would not have been able to act as a team in the here and now, but instead would each have been reacting out of our family-of-origin roles.

After the incident we both had our feelings about the break-in and were able to be there for our son, Aaron, age 3, who was very frightened.

If I had not addressed those past experiences which were affecting me in adulthood, I would have reached out for one of my addictions to cover up my feelings. I would not have been able to heal from the experience and would have continued to carry the trauma with me indefinitely.

Michael would have sheltered himself from his feelings by isolating behind walls and distancing behavior, never feeling his fear, rage and grief about being violated. His feelings would have manifested themselves as headaches or backaches, while mine would have displayed themselves as stomachaches, for which I would have sought out mood-altering medication.

By our not being responsible for our feelings, Aaron would have taken our feelings on, acting out our fear, anger and sadness with bed-wetting, nail-biting, nightmares or aggressive behavior with his playmates. Aaron would have been emotionally abandoned as neither of us would have been emotionally available to him. Instead Aaron did not have to carry our feelings, but was able to be nurtured by two parents who knew how to act responsibly for themselves and him.

The 4th Step in the 12-Step recovery process allows the recovering adult child an opportunity to begin exploring how past childhood events continue to affect the adult living in the here and now. By looking at patterns of behavior and where those patterns have originated, the healing process can begin. Without this type of examination, dysfunctional patterns continue to be acted out indefinitely, many times without awareness.

By bringing these patterns into awareness, choice as to whether to continue acting them out becomes possible. When current-day patterns are connected to old dysfunctional survival skills, the grief process involving the feelings of rage, loneliness, abandonment, shame, fright, sadness and grief can begin. As this process is worked, past traumas and pain are resolved, leaving clear and open the door for healthy self-discovery.

The past and its present-day patterns stunt self-development, leaving one spiritually, emotionally and in many cases physically ill. By "clearing up the wreckage of the past," as is said in 12-Step groups and various pieces of literature, life as it was meant to be can begin.

When most of us get to the 4th Step, there are several different paths we take. The 4th Step states, *"Made a searching and fearless moral inventory of ourselves."* One path a number of folks take is avoidance. They see the world *moral* and freak. "Moral! You mean I have to write out all of my secrets?" The dysfunctional survival skill which says, "If I ignore *it, it* will go away," is at work here.

In the other extreme, many Adult Children see the phrase "make a searching and fearless moral inventory" as an opportunity to exercise the dysfunctional survival skill of *perfectionism.*

Some work so diligently toward perfection that they lose perception of what the 4th Step is really all about. "This is important and I *must* get it right! My handwriting is too sloppy! I need to do it over. It doesn't contain *everything* about me yet, so I'll just put it away for now." These are examples of the survival skill of perfection being acted out with the very tool responsible for exposing such behaviors. Most folks involved in 12-Step movements do *several* 4th Steps because they cannot "get it all down" the first time.

Throughout the recovery process, new memories emerge or awareness surfaces of patterns of behavior previously not recognized. The 4th Step for most is not a one-shot deal. What is not addressed this go-round will be so later on. Do the best you can with what you have, and don't worry about crossing all of the "t's" and dotting all of the "i's." If one of your survival skills is perfection, use this 4th Step as an opportunity to explore where your *need* for this survival skill originated.

A few Adult Children see the word "moral" and almost rejoice in the thought of abusing themselves by focusing on everything immoral about their life. At the same time, many not only exaggerate their so-called immoral behavior, but also take responsibility for the actions of those who have hurt them. Usually what is left out of 4th Steps such as these are the positive and very moral characteristics the Adult Child possesses. Once again dysfunctional survival skills are at work here.

Children have a need to see their major caregivers as healthy and responsible. If they do not see them as such, the feelings of insecurity can be overwhelming. It is not safe for us in childhood to see that our caregivers are abusive or irresponsible. This sets up for children living in dysfunctional families the thought, "They are bigger than me and must know what they are doing, so the problems in my family *have to be my fault.*" This takes the burden of responsibility off the parents, allowing them in the child's mind to be responsible adults who will care for the child.

It becomes safer for children to accept responsibility for the dysfunction in the family because this provides a *false* sense of control. This *false* sense of control provides a *false* sense of safety. Also, children who are abused emotionally, physically, sexually or spiritually carry with them a deep sense of shame which says, "If I weren't so defective, naughty, a problem, worthless, unlovable, dirty or ugly, my family would not be like this." This belief system allows us to always feel personally responsible for most of life's problems, even those we are not responsible for. Once again, it is easier to take responsibility in childhood for the abuse, addiction and dysfunction around us than to see where it really belongs. This is why I will be using the term "survival skills," as opposed to "defects of character."

The term survival skills puts our behaviors in perspective and forces us to look at these behaviors for what they are, as opposed to beating ourselves up with them. You will also be exploring those positive aspects of *you*, and for some, this will be more difficult. "You mean I have to acknowledge my healthy, creative self?" *Yes!*

So now that the ground rules for beginning the 4th Step have been explored, let's proceed, knowing:

1. We don't have to do it perfectly.
2. We don't have to beat ourselves up with our 4th Step.
3. We will discover those creative survival skills which kept us alive in our sick family system.
4. We will learn how these once useful survival skills are no longer serving us in the here and now.
5. And finally, we will discover we now have a choice as to whether or not to hang onto them.

Let's begin . . .

CHAPTER

3

The 4th-Step Adventure

For most, doing a 4th Step seems too vague. There is always a great deal of confusion about, "What is it I am supposed to write about?" When I first began addressing my own unfinished business, I felt overwhelmed. I would ask my therapist, recovery friends and even strangers what it was I was supposed to be putting down on paper.

Unfortunately for the controlling part of me, I had a lot of memory loss about my childhood. At one point I was obsessed with knowing what I didn't know, and I completely lost sight of what it was I did know about my family history. I drove myself nuts trying to pull up a lost memory before it was ready to come up. I also made all those around me batty with my constant whining about lost memory.

What I did not realize at that time was that I was very fortunate to not have complete recall of all of my history. If I had had total recall of my childhood experiences all at once, I would have been a candidate for the nearest lock-up looney bin.

Fortunately for me, my mind had protected me from some very scary trauma by repressing those intense experiences I wasn't ready to deal with. At that time I did not feel safe, secure or confident enough in myself to be able to re-experience the feelings those painful events of the past would eventually provide.

As I gained more strength and recovered, emotionally, I was better prepared to do the work necessary to heal from those experiences. Slowly, when it was time and not a moment sooner, my memories began to emerge. Meantime I had a rare space of insight which said, "Carla, focus on what it is you do know, and stop being so overwhelmed with what you don't know!"

Well, that just about took the breath out of me! I asked myself, "Did I really lack that much in common sense?" This insight seemed so simple and I followed it. It is important to know that this will not be the only 4th Step you will complete if you plan on continuing the recovery process.

Some recovering ACoAs routinely do a 4th Step each year in order to "clean their emotional house" and promote spiritual growth. Others do a 4th Step "as needed" when they are stuck in the recovery process. Everybody works the 12 Steps differently, but remember, you will always have another chance to do a 4th Step. If you have memory loss and are concerned about not being able to include this on a 4th Step, take heart and comfort in knowing that does not have to keep you from working on your current inventory.

Also recognize that as a child your creative mind gave you the gift of not having certain events in your consciousness. When children experience trauma, it is essential that they be allowed to experience all of their feelings about the event by talking about the experience of trauma for as long as necessary.

When our house was broken into, my son Aaron talked continuously about the "bad guy who broke the door." He talked to me, his father, grandparents, playmates, his sitter and the checker in the neighborhood market about the experience. This debriefing allowed him an opportunity to process his feelings of confusion, fear and even anger.

He wore his two toy swords and three squirt guns on his belt and talked about "getting the bad guy!" In this way, he was reclaiming his power and reducing his level of fear. This acting out is healthy because it allows for healing from trauma. Unfortunately a number of us were forced to repress our trauma with the creative child mind, because we were not in safe situations which allowed for such processing.

Some of those childhood family-of-origin situations might have been as follows:

1. It was not safe to talk about our trauma because it might have involved our caretaker's addictive behavior, such as alcoholism, drug abuse, sexual abuse, etc. Since our caretakers were in denial of addiction, we knew talking was pointless.
2. We had to immediately numb ourselves out emotionally and physically in order to protect ourselves from the emotional, physical or sexual abuse of a caretaker.
3. We were shamed, discounted or rejected when we did try to talk about our feelings, our trauma experiences or perceptions of what we saw happening in our family of origin, and we quickly learned it was not safe to feel or talk. Having had to develop the survival skill of repression in childhood, convincing our child mind it is safe to unlock and free our memories from the past will take some time for many of us.

We must be patient with ourselves and the survival skill of repression. What we can do is focus in on those events from childhood which we have conscious memory of. To simplify this process so we are not overwhelmed, it is useful to divide our life from the beginning to the present into manageable blocks of time.

For example, we could separate our life as follows:

Age 1–5   The Early Years
Age 5–10   The Learning Years
Age 10–15   The Exploring years
Age 15-20   More Growing Years

All of these titles will be defined as we address each individual age group in our 4th Step.

It might also be useful to document for ourselves what feelings we did experience during each age group. Most of us will feel overwhelmed with this statement, replying, "How am I supposed to know how I was feeling, especially if it wasn't okay to have feelings in my family?"

Believe it or not, we did experience feelings during our childhood but for the most part our primary feeling may have been *numb*. Numb is a feeling! Most of us are also experts at chastising ourselves for not understanding that the feeling *numb* was a *survival skill* which protected us when it wasn't safe to feel other feelings.

If we remember feeling numb a lot, this is only another indicator of how unsafe and unacceptable it was to express our feelings full force. Other feelings we may have had in childhood might have included *terror, rage, grief, abandonment, loneliness, joy, love* and *security*. Along with this, we may also wish to examine how we responded to certain childhood events, such as the anger of an alcoholic father, the death of a parent, the physical pain of a slap in the face or the betrayal of a broken promise.

When we experience dysfunctional behavior from our family members and do not have the healthy tools a healthy family can provide for resolving life trauma, our creative child mind develops survival skills to suit the situation. Though these work in childhood, in adulthood they become the basis for co-dependent behavior and adult dysfunction.

Examining our responses to trauma and exploring how these patterns of behavior continue to be acted out in adulthood can provide for us a wealth of information. With this information we can begin making changes in our lives and develop those skills necessary for healthy adult living. Once we have done this, it will also be necessary to take a look at how we feel today about our childhood history.

This is our unfinished business. Our unfinished business continues to haunt us until we give it the attention it deserves. To only acknowledge it, without working through it, is to once again deny our history's impact on us in the here and now.

Resolving our unfinished business is a process and we have a lifetime to do it. It is important to know that commitment to resolving our unfinished business is what is essential to our growth. Today I continue to work through my own unfinished business as it is appropriate. In early recovery, I thought there was some sort of prize for tying up *all* unfinished business.

I almost wore myself out tackling one issue after another, believing I had to have it all *done* in a certain amount of time. Doing it this way, I did not really complete resolving each incident of trauma. I also began to burn myself out on my own recovery program. I was disillusioned, depressed and overwhelmed. And, to my dismay, I discovered I had *more* than I had originally expected to address. Taking our unfinished business as it comes, one piece at a time, ensures successful recovery from childhood trauma.

The 4th Step begins to identify for us those issues we must commit to address. Then working toward resolution at a pace *we can handle* produces the many gifts of recovery. Now that we have some established guidelines set for beginning our inventory, let's take a look at the category entitled "The Early Years."

Our core personality is established by age five, according to many developmental psychologists. All one needs to do is open an introductory psychology text to read about how important stability is for the youngster age five and under. For those of us who grew up in an alcoholic, drug-dependent, food-addicted, work-obsessed, religiously addicted, sex-dependent or whatever-addicted home, we know from experience that life was anything but stable. For our purposes, it is important to have some understanding about what a healthy family looks like so we have a baseline for examining our own family system. The characteristics of a healthy family are as follows.

Characteristics Of A Functional Healthy Family

A. Flexible regarding roles and rules.
B. Parents have the ability to take control in healthy ways.
C. Expectations are communicated.
D. Family members take responsibility for their own feelings, behaviors and attitudes.
E. Parents have a life of their own . . . away from the children.
F. Family members respect each other.
G. Family has the ability to adapt to change.
H. The basic needs for food, clothing, shelter, medical attention and healthy touch are satisfied.
 I. Members have the ability to listen and empathize with others.
 J. Sense of unity and belonging, with each family member having their own identity and boundaries.
K. Members trust each other.
L. There is a sense of humor and the ability to laugh with each other.
M. The ability to grow and learn is within the family system.
N. Family members fight fairly.
O. Family members agree that it is all right to disagree.

Now compare your family system with the characteristics of the family with health. List below and describe how your family system and a healthy family system are alike:

1. _____
2. _____
3. _____
4. _____

List and describe how your family system differs from those characteristics of a healthy family system.

1. _____
2. _____
3. _____
4. _____

Describe those characteristics of the healthy family system you feel you *need* in your own life today.

1. _____
2. _____
3. _____
4. _____

List and describe any feelings you have about not having had a number of healthy characteristics of a functional family system in your family of origin. For example, "I feel cheated, I feel at a loss, I feel ill-prepared for life."

1. _____
2. _____
3. _____
4. _____

List and describe those healthy characteristics you would like to implement into your life in the here and now.

1. _____
2. _____
3. _____
4. _____

Tools for assisting you in doing this will be discussed later on.

Jill's Story

S mall children need the security of a healthy environment while growing up to be able to live life successfully in adulthood. The characteristics previously described, which define a healthy family, give children those skills which will allow them to evolve into the functional, creative, joyous beings we were all meant to be.

During my early childhood, I was constantly guarding myself because my family system was addictive, rageful and at times very abusive. As a consequence of this, I grew into an adult who was addicted to alcohol, drugs, food and more. I also was a rageaholic who continually would lose total control of my emotions, only to feel intense shame after a volcanic blast. On top of all of this, most of my adult relationships were very abusive and I continually played the role of a victim who would seek out the worst offenders.

Even though I had quit drinking, drugging and eating addictively, my poor behavior patterns established between the ages of one and five continued to affect me greatly. After discovering what a healthy family system was supposed to look like, I had a baseline to compare my own with. I finally was able to say "Holy Cow! I've got something to shoot for!"

When we begin to look at our own dysfunctional behavior patterns, survival skills or defects of character, it is always important to start at the beginning. Now that we have a bit of an understanding of what a healthy system looks like and have had a chance to compare our family of origin with this healthy system, it is time to begin moving from generalities to specifics. In order to see how our childhood Early Years have affected us and how they continue to affect our living today, we need to write out those resentments we are carrying toward our parents, siblings, grandparents, aunts, uncles and other caretakers.

These resentments usually come in the form of, "I feel wronged because . . .," or "My angry feelings are related to . . .," or "I still get upset when I think about . . .," and are easy to identify. Other types of resentments which are usually more difficult to identify are buried in pain or numbness. Because the feeling anger does not appear to be present, these resentments may go unnoticed.

For example, Jill was physically abused at age four by her mother when she did not clean her room perfectly. Jill's mother was a perfectionist and would become terribly upset if every toy was not in its proper place and every article of clothing put away where it belonged. Jill was not capable of maintaining her mother's high standard of perfection and would instead clean her room like an imperfect, normal four-year-old.

Outraged upon seeing Jill's cleaning job, Jill's mother would tell her to go to the backyard to the willow tree and pick a switch for her whipping. Confused, she would get her switch, strip it of leaves and hand it to her mother. Her mother would then tell her, "I am doing this for your own good. You know this will hurt me much more than it will hurt you." She would end this lecture with, "No tears, Jill, take your medicine like a big girl," and Jill would receive her whipping.

During such abusive experiences, Jill learned to numb her emotions in order to survive her mother's rage and shut her body down to keep from feeling the stinging pain of the whippings. She survived well, but in adulthood she feels powerless and toolless in the world of grownups. She does not know how to take care of herself on the job, in relationships or in her current family situation with her husband and two daughters.

On her job, Jill is taken advantage of on a regular basis. Her peers at work constantly dump extra work on her. On top of the pressure of this excessive workload, Jill insists that her work be done perfectly. Because of her need for perfection and her inability to say, "No," "I'm too busy," or even, "Do it yourself," she is constantly overwhelmed and feels she can never catch up. Jill even carts work home with her on weekends in an attempt to "gain control," but her life continues to be unmanageable.

At home Jill's husband George can be emotionally cruel and at times physically abusive. George is an active workaholic and alcoholic. When he has had too much to drink, is hungover or wanting a drink, he can be painfully sharp with words. Periodically when in a rage, George will push Jill harshly or even strike her. As during her childhood, Jill numbs out emotionally and physically to avoid painful blows. But after such experiences she compulsively cleans, focuses all of her attention on the children or eats too much. She never connects that these dysfunctional behaviors are related to being abused by her husband, which is directly tied back to her unresolved trauma with her mother.

Because George is emotionally unavailable to their two daughters, Jill goes out of her way to be the perfect mother. She does not want to be like her mother, so she swings 180° in the opposite direction and really does not provide guidelines or healthy discipline for her children. Jill does not have control over her children, and they basically run her, her life and the house. Whatever they want, whenever they want it and no matter how much money it costs, Jill provides it.

Jill entered therapy because she felt out of control with her children and like a failure as a parent. She shared about her childhood relationship with her mother but stated, "That really didn't affect me." She truly believes this statement of denial because over the years she has distanced herself emotionally from the original experience in order to survive her childhood.

After working with Jill's family history, her therapist asked, "Why did your father and mother divorce?" Jill said, "Because my mom thought he drank too much," and quickly followed this with, "But he wasn't an alcoholic or anything like that." Her therapist gave her a look of surprise and handed her some basic information on alcoholism. During her next session, her therapist described for her the emotional characteristics that those growing up in alcoholic homes have in common.

These characteristics, developed by Tony A. and termed the "Laundry List" in ACoA meetings, are as follows:

The Laundry List By Tony A.

1. We became isolated and afraid of people and authority figures.
2. We are frightened by angry people and personal criticism.
3. We became approval seekers and lost our identity in the process.
4. We either become alcoholics, marry them or both — or find another compulsive personality, such as a workaholic, to fulfill our sick abandonment needs.
5. We live life from the viewpoint of victims and are attracted by that weakness in our love and friendship relationships.
6. We have an overdeveloped sense of responsibility and it is easier for us to be concerned with others rather than ourselves. This enables us not to look too closely at our own faults.
7. We have guilt feelings when we stand up for ourselves and instead give in to others.
8. We confuse love and pity and tend to "love" people we can pity and rescue.
9. We became addicted to excitement.
10. We have stuffed our feelings from our traumatic childhoods and have lost the ability to feel or express our feelings because it hurts too much. (Denial)
11. We judge ourselves harshly and have a very low sense of self-esteem.
12. We are dependent personalities who are terrified of abandonment and will do anything to hold onto a relationship in order not to experience the painful abandonment feelings we received from living with sick people who were never there emotionally for us.

After reading this, Jill's eyes became tearful. She began to see her initial complaint about her childrearing practices was much more complex than she originally thought. Her basic problems are related to her own upbringing. She began to realize that her situation with her husband is directly related to her family-of-origin experiences with her parents, and that even her difficulties on the job are tied into the picture. Jill was stunned.

If we were to use Jill's experiences as an example of how to get on paper the way her childhood experiences relate to her current situation, we would first want to determine what her resentments are. Several of these resentments are as follows:

Resentment

1. Mother demanding perfection.
2. Having an alcoholic father.
3. Mother whipping Jill.

In order to completely understand how these past issues continue to affect the here and now, we need some guidelines in writing out resentments. The following page, using Jill's situation as an example, is a guide for beginning this process.

From *The Laundry List: The ACoA Experience* by Tony A. and Dan F., Deerfield Beach, FL: Health Communications, 1991.

SURVIVAL SKILLS — EARLY YEARS INVENTORY 0-5

I.	II.	III.	IV.	V.	VI.
Hurt, resentment — person, place, time. (Facts only)	How I felt about it then.	How I feel about it now. (Unfinished business)	What I did in response to the situation. (Survival skills, co-dependent behavior)	What I would do today in a similar situation. (Recovery)	Action I need to take to heal from this experience. (Anger Work, Grief Work)
1. When I was 4, living with my mother, she would rage at me for not clean-ing my room as she liked it.	*Numb Confused Scared*	*Angry Hurt*	*Tried to block it out.*	*Would tell the rager their behavior was abusive and leave.*	
2. When I was 3, my father and mother divorced because of my father's drinking.	*Numb Lonely Shame*	*Rage Grief Abandon-ment Shame*	*Ignored it*	*Express my feelings about what I was feeling.*	
3. When I was 4, my mother expected me to clean my room perfectly.	*Frustrated Hopeless Inadequate A failure Unloved*	*Rage Grief*	*Tried harder*	*Tell her I was doing the best I could and that I did not have to do it perfectly.*	

Once Jill was able to write out her resentments using this format, she was able to see several things:

A. What her unfinished business was.
B. How her survival skills originated.
C. How much healthy thinking she did possess today in adulthood.

After examining her early years, it was necessary for Jill to explore those situations in the present which paralleled her childhood. We continue to repeat those dysfunctional behavioral patterns we have learned along the road of childhood until the trauma of our youth is addressed. The following is an example of how we can take a resentment in adulthood and map it out the same way we did resentments in childhood.

ADULT INVENTORY I

I. Hurt, resentment — person, place, time. (Facts only)	II. How I felt about it then.	III. How I feel about it now. (Unfinished business)	IV. What I did in response to the situation. (Survival skills, co-dependent behavior)	V. What I would do today in a similar situation. (Recovery)	VI. Action I need to take to heal from this experience. (Anger Work, Grief Work)
1. George got drunk at our Christmas party.	Embarrassed Ashamed Fearful Alone	Rage Grief Abandoned Shame	Covered up his behavior and made excuses for his drunkenness.	I would not cover up for him and I would express my feelings.	
2. Judy at work dumped her share of work on my desk last week.	Frustrated Confused Hopeless Inadequate Alone	Rageful Discounted Unimportant Abandoned	I would just try hard to get it done.	I would tell her to do it herself, that I was busy.	
3. George had a hangover and was very angry last month. One night he slapped my face and pushed me.	Numb Scared Powerless	Rage Hurt Rejected Unloved	I would just numb myself out and take it, hoping he would quit.	I would protect my-self, go to a friend's house, call the police.	

Having done the Early Years Survival Skill Inventory and the Adulthood Survival Skill Inventory, it is time to take a look at any similarities between the two. Some patterns of behavior are extraordinarily obvious, while others take a bit more examination. Look closely at Jill's two Inventories and see if you can pick out the similar patterns.

List one pattern you can identify in both.

1. _____

_____

Some of the patterns which are apparent in both inventories are:

a. Jill numbs out emotional and physical pain in adulthood as she did in childhood.
   Survival Skill: Numbing Out
b. Jill doesn't express her true feelings to peers and authority figures, as she did not in childhood. She stuffs her feelings for fear of upsetting others and also in order to protect herself from future abuse and rejection.
   Survival Skill: Stuffing Feelings
c. Jill accepts responsibility for other people's feelings and workloads, believing she is at fault if they are not happy — just as she did in childhood when her mother demanded perfection. She doesn't allow others to be responsible — her husband for his alcoholism and rage, her peers for their workload, her children for their inappropriate behavior — as she didn't know her mother was responsible for her abusive behavior and her father for his alcoholism.
   Survival Skill: Enabling by accepting responsibility for others when not appropriate.

After Jill had examined what her survival skills were, where and why they had originated and how they were being acted out in the here and now, she needed some *solutions* for resolving them. Jill needed tools which would help her to heal from the original trauma.

By healing the original trauma, she could then begin to develop those tools necessary for healing from the feelings of resentment, pain and powerlessness she experienced today. Everybody works the healing process a little bit differently, but the primary feelings which must be expressed and embraced about our past trauma and present resentments are:

- Anger
- Grief
- Shame
- Abandonment.

CHAPTER

5

Beginning The 4th Step With The Early Years

As we have discovered by examining Jill's Inventories, it is clear that she continues to carry feelings from childhood trauma. By identifying this problem area, by discovering the origins of such feelings and by determining how these feelings are being manifested in the here and now, the healing process can begin.

Like Jill, it is necessary for us to begin to inventory our past. As Jill did, we too will begin by listing those events from our past which we:

- Continue to think about
- Harbor feelings for
- Are confused by
- Feel uncomfortable with
- Have been told are traumatic, abnormal or abusive.

For now, limit this inventory to ages one through five years.

As discussed earlier, we may have feelings about these events or be numb when writing them out. Remember, both responses are common. If necessary, refer to the following information on abuse to clarify what childhood experiences may have been abusive for you during these years. If you have memory loss of these years, do not be alarmed. For trauma survivors this is *normal*. Memory loss will be more fully addressed later on.

It is *normal* to either have intense feelings as a result of reviewing these checklists or to be numb. This checklist will assist you in writing up your own inventories. Refer to it when necessary. Now let's begin with our Early Years Inventory.

The following is a checklist for possible unresolved abuse issues from childhood. Check those that apply to you:

Emotional Abuse

_____ Name-calling (dumb, idiot, ugly, airhead, screwup, etc.)
_____ The silent treatment.
_____ Shaming one into doing something ("If you had a brain, you would do it . . .")
_____ Exposure to raging behavior.
_____ Being raged at.
_____ Being shamed for having certain feelings.
_____ Being shamed for talking or having an opinion.
_____ Demand for perfection from caregivers.
_____ Being compared to another.
_____ Using God, the Bible or religion as a method of control or as a punishment.
_____ Being told what you see, hear or feel is imagined, wrong or not really happening.
_____ Being told to not tell when hurt by another.

Physical Abuse

_____ Face slapping
_____ Hitting, whipping
_____ Beating with fists, belts, coat hangers, tree branches, hair brushes, kitchen utensils

_____ Harsh shoving
_____ Excessive tickling
_____ Hair pulling
_____ Deprivation of physical needs: food, clothing, shelter, healthy physical touch and emotional attention
_____ Abandonment
_____ Lack of medical attention
_____ Over-protection
_____ A lack of healthy emotional guidance
_____ Being isolated from others.

Indirect Sexual Abuse
(Abuse Which Is Not On Purpose, But Is Still Abusive)

_____ A lack of privacy or boundaries
_____ Parents having affairs
_____ Parents sexually acting out inappropriately
_____ Shamed for being male or female
_____ Face slapping
_____ Enemas or other intrusive medical procedures
_____ Living with parents who have not dealt with their sexual abuse issues
_____ Exposure to excessive nudity
_____ Sleeping with parents on a regular basis (being used as a shield between parents, serving as a parent's sleep mate)
_____ Bathing with parents after age four
_____ Being bathed by a parent after child has set a boundary
_____ Living with parents who have difficulty with their own sexuality (dislike for sex, excessive need for sex or sexually addicted, with gender issues)
_____ Little or lack of healthy information about sexuality and development
_____ Too much information about sex too soon
_____ Emotional incest, or being the substitute spouse, friend, confidant, junior therapist, problem-solver, message-carrier, comforter, parent, etc. for a caregiver.

Direct Sexual Abuse

_____ Exposure to pornography

_____ Inappropriate touching, hugging, kissing or dancing with an adult or older child during childhood

_____ Exposure to adult sexual activities, such as acts of sex, movies, games, bars, strip joints, adult book stores

_____ Being masturbated or used for masturbation

_____ Penetration with fingers or other implements

_____ Being forced to perform oral sex by a caregiver or older child

_____ Being forced into anal sex by a caregiver or older child

_____ Being forced into intercourse by a caregiver or older child

_____ Having sex with an adult or older child, even if it feels pleasurable

_____ Rape, date rape, rape in a marriage

_____ Using acts of sex as a way of nurturing a child

_____ Children being told because the act of sex was pleasurable it was all right and the adults involved were not wrong

_____ Telling a parent about being sexually abused and that parent shaming, not investigating or not taking the child seriously

_____ Being told not to tell when abused

_____ Being forced to act out sexually with other children.

Other Instances Of Unresolved Trauma

_____ Parental divorce

_____ Death of a parent, sibling, close relative or pet

_____ Serious childhood illnesses .

_____ Living with a parent who has been involved in a war or other trauma

_____ Living with addiction to work, religion, alcohol, drugs, food, money, co-dependency, sex, etc.

_____ Living in poverty

_____ Loss of home, safety, security

_____ Witnessing a death

_____ Exposure to murder or brutal violence

_____ Living with adults involved in illegal activity

_____ Living with parents who are untreated adult children

_____ Living with parents who are holocaust survivors or whose parents are holocaust survivors.

SURVIVAL SKILLS — EARLY YEARS INVENTORY 1-5

I.	II.	III.	IV.	V.	VI.
Hurt, resentment — person, place, time. (Facts only)	How I felt about it then.	How I feel about it now. (Unfinished business)	What I did in response to the situation. (Survival skills, co-dependent behavior)	What I would do today in a similar situation. (Recovery)	Action I need to take to heal from this experience. (Anger Work, Grief Work)

Now that you have completed your Early Years Inventory, try to list those hurts and resentments in the here and now which are similar to your experiences between the ages of birth and five. For some of you this will be quite easy to do, whereas for others it will feel impossible. Do the best you can and know that if you forget to inventory an incident in this section, you will have plenty of opportunity down the road.

SURVIVAL SKILLS — ADULT INVENTORY

I.	II.	III.	IV.	V.	VI.
Hurt, resentment — person, place, time. (Facts only)	How I felt about it then.	How I feel about it now. (Unfinished business)	What I did in response to the situation. (Survival skills, co-dependent behavior)	What I would do today in a similar situation. (Recovery)	Action I need to take to heal from this experience. (Anger Work, Grief Work)

Having listed this information, it is time to familiarize ourselves with what was happening in our lives between the ages of one and five. We can do this by gathering together as many photographs of ourselves as possible from that time. It is important to note how we react when looking at these photographs, and we may want to journal our feelings.

Some examples of journal entries might be:

"When I look at a picture of myself at age three, I feel sad."

"When I examine the child I was at age five, I don't have any strong feelings that I can identify, but my stomach feels queasy or upset."

For those of us who have memory loss, this is an excellent way to gently pull up our repressed memory of these ages. It is a slow process, so be easy with yourself and limit your expectations of memory recall.

Journal your feelings as you look at the photographs on a daily basis for two weeks. This gives you an opportunity to observe your own progress. Each day you will have a small new awareness. You may begin recalling your lost memory in symbolic dreams or vivid memory.

Always keep a pad and pencil near your bed and write out any dreams or feelings you have upon awakening. If you have dreams which are symbolic, spend some time writing out what each symbol in your dream means to you. Believe it or not, *we* are the best interpreters of our own dreams.

After completing the Childhood Survival Skills Inventory, journaling your feelings about your photographs and documenting your dreams and feelings upon awakening, it is time to take a closer look at our:

1. Survival skills
2. Unfinished business
3. Recovery skills

The survival skills we developed in childhood kept us emotionally distant from the dysfunction in our addicted family systems. For our purposes, we will list only those survival skills we have been able to identify as a consequence of our Childhood Inventory. Later on there will be plenty of time to list other survival skills as we discover them.

It might be useful to refer to Jill's Survival Skill List, which was discussed earlier, to give us a basis as to how to list our own. Refer to the sections underlined *Survival Skills* in looking at Jill's example. Also refer to your Childhood Inventory and the column titled "What I Did in Response to the Situation" in helping you compose your own list.

Survival Skills

My Survival Skills Which Originated From Ages One To Five

   Example: Numbing Out Feelings

   1. _____
   2. _____
   3. _____
   4. _____

How I Feel About Each Survival Skill (angry, sad, ashamed, confused)

   Example: Frustrated, powerless

   1. _____
   2. _____
   3. _____
   4. _____

How Does Each Survival Skill Cause Unmanageability Or Problems In My Life Today?

   Example: I have difficulty feeling other feelings.

   1. _____
   2. _____
   3. _____
   4. _____

How Have I Tried To Control, Alter, Ignore, Fix Or Minimize Each Of My Survival Skills?

Example: By denying my family dysfunction.

   1. _____

   2. _____

   3. _____

   4. _____

What Is My Payoff For These Survival Skills?

Example: I don't have to admit my family was dysfunctional and have any feelings about this.

   1. _____

   2. _____

   3. _____

   4. _____

What Price Or Losses Are My Survival Skills Costing Me Today In The Here And Now?

Example: When somebody else's behavior is abusive to me, I deny it and don't stand up for myself. (Loss of self-respect, self-esteem and emotional safety.)

   1. _____

   2. _____

   3. _____

   4. _____

How Did My Survival Skills Protect Me While Growing Up In My Family?

Example: By being numb as a child, I didn't have to feel how crazy my family was. My false sense of security protected me and kept me emotionally distant.

    1. _____

    2. _____

    3. _____

    4. _____

It is important to examine, not only how our survival skills are disrupting our adult life, but how they provided us with gifts for survival while growing up.

What Payoffs Or Gifts Did I Receive From My Survival Skills While Growing Up?

Example: A belief which said, "No matter what happens to me, I will not let them see me hurt!" False sense of control.

    1. _____

    2. _____

    3. _____

    4. _____

Unfinished Business

It is now time to determine what unfinished business we continue to carry with us as a consequence of our family-of-origin dysfunction. To identify this, it is necessary to look at the column in the Inventory headed "How I Feel About It Now." List the different feelings you continue to carry about your family-of-origin history between the ages of one and five (rage, shame, numbness, fear).

Example: Grief.

1. _____
2. _____
3. _____
4. _____

List what each feeling is related to in your family-of-origin history. Follow the examples below by listing those feelings you carry about your unfinished business from childhood and the incidents related to these feelings.

Example: I have *grief* that my mother and father were too preoccupied with the disease of alcoholism to be there emotionally for me. I also have grief about:

a. Dad yelling at me when drunk.
b. Grandma dying and nobody talking about it.
c. Never feeling good enough, perfect enough.
d. Mom never saying she loved me.

1. _____
   a. _____
   b. _____
   c. _____
   d. _____
2. _____
   a. _____
   b. _____

c. _____

d. _____

3. _____

   a. _____

   b. _____

   c. _____

   d. _____

4. _____

   a. _____

   b. _____

   c. _____

   d. _____

Listing the above can be very painful and at the same time enlightening. Once we know what our unfinished business is, we can take action to resolve it.

After I began to discover what had happened to me in my childhood, my first thought was "Okay, so now what?" I had finally connected my feelings (which for so long were "free floating" and not really connected to anything) to some really painful stuff in my past. I remember being very upset because I initially thought that by recalling these events I *would be fixed!*

The big shock was that I seemed to be in *more* pain than before. I said to myself, "Screw this recovery stuff! This is for the birds! Denial wasn't great, but it was better than this!" At that point I *hated* recovery.

What I didn't know at the time was that I needed to take some action.

In order to complete our inventory, it is necessary to determine what action steps are needed to begin resolving our own unfinished business. There are several ways to address this, but the most effective path involves writing letters.

Refer back to Jill's first inventory and look at the unfinished business she has to address from her childhood. Each incident involves painful feelings about treatment received from a family member. There are two columns in her inventory which are specifically for recovery, resolution and action. Healing begins in columns five and six.

Under column V the heading is, *"What I Would Do Today in a Similar Situation."* This column allows for brainstorming about alternative healthy behaviors, as opposed to those unhealthy behaviors listed under, *"What I Did in Response to the Situation."* It provides for us a chance to re-evaluate our survival skills. It is always important to have several options available when we are confronted with a difficult situation. Though you already have one listed, go ahead and list a few more just in case the one listed for some reason doesn't work.

My Options

Incident One: Options for Future Similar Situations.

a. _____
b. _____
c. _____

Incident Two: Options for Future Similar Situations.

a. _____
b. _____
c. _____

Incident Three: Options for Future Similar Situations.

a. _____
b. _____
c. _____

Incident Four: Options for Future Similar Situations.

a. _____
b. _____
c. _____

Incident Five: Options for Future Similar Situations.

a. _____
b. _____
c. _____

Back to column VI and our unfinished business. It will be of benefit to us to write letters to those who have hurt us in the past. It is *important* to note that this does not necessarily mean we will send these letters, so do not worry about this. If those who have caused you pain are dead or if you have not seen them for a long time, it is still necessary to write to them.

You may be asking, "What on earth am I supposed to write to these people about?" Many of us also need guidelines for letter writing. Following are some suggestions which may be of assistance to you.

What To Address In Your Letter

A. Include any feelings you have about the incidents you have listed on your inventory. For example, "When you were drinking, I felt angry, abandoned, sad." In other words, write out your resentments and feelings about those situations.

B. In the letter, it is also important to write out what you lost as a consequence of a family member's behavior. For example, "Because of your drinking, I never had you as a father. I feel sad because you were never there to parent me." "Because you molested me, I never knew what it felt like to feel safe. Because of your abuse, I lost out on learning what safety felt like."

C. Finally, it is important to state in the letter what it is you have always wanted from this person. For example, "I have always wanted to hear you say you loved me." "I always wanted you to appreciate the good grades I got." "I always wanted you to say you were sorry."

D. To finish a letter such as this, it is empowering to state what you are going to do to heal from your pain with this person. Examples of this are as follows:

  1. I will be angry with you for as long as I need to be. I will beat the sofa with a tennis racket when I feel angry with you.

  2. I will have my pain about being physically abused by you by sharing my pain and grief with others in my support group.

3. I will visualize the shame I carry about your drinking. I will visualize where I carry it in my body and what color it is. In my morning meditation I will see myself giving this shame to you.

Now that you have some guidelines for writing, go ahead and begin putting together your letters. Don't worry about doing it perfectly, dotting all the "i's" and crossing all the "t's" with perfect spelling and punctuation. Obsessing on perfection really defeats the purpose. Some of you may feel numb writing your letters, while others may experience intense feelings.

If at all possible, have a photograph of yourself as a young child and a picture of the person you are writing to present during this time. Write these letters at a time when you will not be disturbed. Let your supports know what you are doing, so you can call on them after you have completed these letters.

For myself, I could only do one letter at a time. I also needed some time between letters to process and heal from my feelings. If this is your situation, give yourself permission to take all the time you need. There isn't any need to race through this part of your inventory. Be gentle with yourself.

Take time to write your letter before reading further.

Sharing

Now that you have completed your letters, it is time to decide what you would like to do with them. It will be necessary to share them with someone during a formal 5th Step.

> "Admitting to God, to ourselves, and to another human being the exact nature of our wrongs,"

involves sharing with a therapist, sponsor, recovering friend or clergy person what you have discovered while doing your 4th Step.

After doing your 5th Step, you can:

A. Burn your letters.
B. Send them to the people they are addressed to.

C. Visualize the person they are addressed to and read them out loud.

D. Bury them in your back yard.

I have used The Early Years, ages one through five, as an example to explain how to begin your 4th Step. In addressing the later years (The Learning Years, ages 5 through 10; The Exploring Years, ages 10-15; and More Growing Years, ages 15-20) our 4th Step is basically the same as that used in The Early Years Inventory. From here on out, you will be writing about these years as you did with the Early Years. If you feel confused while addressing the later years, refer back to the examples and explanations provided in previous pages.

CHAPTER

6

The Learning Years

Ages 5-10, The Learning Years

During these years, children learn how to socialize with others by observing how their family members interact with them and with each other. This is also the time when most children begin to move away from the family as they attend school. A child's circle of encounters grows larger through interacting with schoolmates while exploration of life outside of the family begins. If the family is a healthy one, the child will feel safe exploring social situations. This is because children apply the rules, values and traditions they have encountered in their family system to the world in general.

If the family has been safe and supportive, the child will view the world as basically safe and supportive. If children are allowed to develop boundaries by having their bodies, privacy and opinions valued while growing during The Early Years, they will know they have a right to take care of themselves in relationships outside the family system. When children do feel unsafe in the real world, they can return to the safety of the family system for guidance and nurturing.

When the family system is dysfunctional, the world outside of the family also seems dysfunctional to small children. Children who are not allowed boundaries within their family grow into school-age children who don't know how to take care of themselves in healthy ways with other children.

Finally when a family system is dysfunctional, it doesn't always feel safe to go to the family when the world outside feels so scary. Messages like, "Be strong," "Don't be such a baby," or non-verbal messages which communicate, "Don't bother me," keep children from getting their needs taken care of.

The following section will allow you to explore your own Learning Years. Take your time, let your friends and supports know what you are doing — and remember, you don't have to do it perfectly. Let's look at your resentments, unresolved trauma and pain which originated between the ages of five and ten.

SURVIVAL SKILLS — EARLY YEARS INVENTORY 1-5

I.	II.	III.	IV.	V.	VI.
Hurt, resentment — person, place, time. (Facts only)	How I felt about it then.	How I feel about it now. (Unfinished business)	What I did in response to the situation. (Survival skills, co-dependent behavior)	What I would do today in a similar situation. (Recovery)	Action I need to take to heal from this experience. (Anger Work, Grief Work)

As we did with The Early Years, it is also necessary to write out any present-day situations which may be similar to those of The Learning Years. For example, during my Learning Years I was violated by a babysitter. During that time I didn't dream of telling my parents, let alone any other authority figure. I had learned authority figures were not to be trusted.

As an adult I also found myself in work situations with authority figures who had the characteristics of those I had grown up with. As a consequence of this, I responded to them as I had with adults I had grown up with during the Learning Years. If I felt violated or taken advantage of in the workplace by other workers or by my bosses, I would keep this to myself, not trusting anybody or knowing I had a right to take care of myself.

Look at the incidents listed on your inventory for The Learning Years. List how those situations are being repeated in adulthood with peers, associates, family, lover, children or spouse today in different situations, but with patterns similar to your childhood experiences.

SURVIVAL SKILLS — INVENTORY — ADULT II

I.	II.	III.	IV.	V.	VI.
Hurt, resentment — person, place, time. (Facts only)	How I felt about it then.	How I feel about it now. (Unfinished business)	What I did in response to the situation. (Survival skills, co-dependent behavior)	What I would do today in a similar situation. (Recovery)	Action I need to take to heal from this experience. (Anger Work, Grief Work)

1. List the similar patterns of behavior you can identify in both inventories.

a. Pattern _____
_____
_____

Survival Skill or purpose of behavior _____
_____
_____

b. Pattern _____
_____
_____

Survival Skill or purpose of behavior _____
_____
_____

c. Pattern _____
_____
_____

Survival Skill or purpose of behavior _____
_____
_____

d. Pattern _____
_____
_____

Survival Skill or purpose of behavior _____
_____
_____

Find some pictures of yourself which correspond to your Learning Years, ages five through ten. Spend some time looking through them and journal any thoughts, feelings or memories you have of these times.

When I look at pictures of myself between the ages of five and 10, I feel, remember or think of _____
_____

Sometimes we will have dreams about ourselves or about children who are between the ages of five and ten while we are inventorying these years. Usually when we dream about other children, we are really dreaming about ourselves in childhood. Journal any dreams you have had about this age period.

_____

_____

_____

_____

_____

_____

_____

Now it is time to examine those survival skills we developed during The Learning Years. Refer back to your list work on the similarities of your *Learning Years Inventory* and *Adult Inventory II*. List the survival skills you identified in both inventories.

Survival Skills

My Survival Skills Which Originated From Ages Five To Ten

1. _____

2. _____

3. _____

4. _____

How I Feel About Each Survival Skill (numb, sad, angry, confused)

1. _____

2. _____

3. _____

4. _____

How Does Each Survival Skill Cause Unmanageability Or Problems In My Life Today?

1. _____
2. _____
3. _____
4. _____

How Have I Tried To Control, Alter, Ignore, Fix Or Minimize Each Of My Survival Skills?

1. _____
2. _____
3. _____
4. _____

What Is My Payoff For These Survival Skills?

1. _____
2. _____
3. _____
4. _____

What Price Or Losses Are My Survival Skills Costing Me Today In The Here And Now?
(Loss Of Self-Esteem, Self-Respect, Financial, Emotional, Social)

1. _____
2. _____
3. _____
4. _____

How Did My Survival Skills Protect Me While Growing Up In My Family?

1. _____
2. _____

3. _____

4. _____

What Payoffs Or Gifts Did I Receive From My
Survival Skills While Growing Up?

1. _____

2. _____

3. _____

4. _____

Unfinished Business

Look at your Learning Years Inventory Column III entitled
"Unfinished Business." List the unfinished business or feelings
you continue to carry regarding your family history.

Feelings: Rage, Shame, Grief, Loneliness, Fear, Numbness.

1. _____

2. _____

3. _____

4. _____

List the incident each feeling is related to on your inventory
and then list any other unfinished business which evokes this
feeling for you.

1. Incident: _____

_____

_____

• Other unfinished business evoking this feeling: _____

_____

_____

2. Incident: _____

_____

_____

• Other unfinished business evoking this feeling: ＿＿＿＿

＿＿＿＿＿＿＿＿＿＿＿＿＿＿＿＿＿＿＿＿＿＿＿＿＿＿

＿＿＿＿＿＿＿＿＿＿＿＿＿＿＿＿＿＿＿＿＿＿＿＿＿＿

3. Incident: ＿＿＿＿＿＿＿＿＿＿＿＿＿＿＿＿＿＿＿＿＿

＿＿＿＿＿＿＿＿＿＿＿＿＿＿＿＿＿＿＿＿＿＿＿＿＿＿

• Other unfinished business evoking this feeling: ＿＿＿＿

＿＿＿＿＿＿＿＿＿＿＿＿＿＿＿＿＿＿＿＿＿＿＿＿＿＿

＿＿＿＿＿＿＿＿＿＿＿＿＿＿＿＿＿＿＿＿＿＿＿＿＿＿

4. Incident: ＿＿＿＿＿＿＿＿＿＿＿＿＿＿＿＿＿＿＿＿＿

＿＿＿＿＿＿＿＿＿＿＿＿＿＿＿＿＿＿＿＿＿＿＿＿＿＿

• Other unfinished business evoking this feeling: ＿＿＿＿

＿＿＿＿＿＿＿＿＿＿＿＿＿＿＿＿＿＿＿＿＿＿＿＿＿＿

＿＿＿＿＿＿＿＿＿＿＿＿＿＿＿＿＿＿＿＿＿＿＿＿＿＿

Now it's time to examine any unfinished business we have as a consequence of our *Adult II Inventory*. Look at Column III and write out all of your unfinished business, incident by incident, and any feelings you continue to carry as a consequence of the incidents listed in this section.

1. Incident: ＿＿＿＿＿＿＿＿＿＿＿＿＿＿＿＿＿＿＿＿

＿＿＿＿＿＿＿＿＿＿＿＿＿＿＿＿＿＿＿＿＿＿＿＿＿＿

Feeling: ＿＿＿＿＿＿＿＿＿＿＿＿＿＿＿＿＿＿＿＿＿＿

＿＿＿＿＿＿＿＿＿＿＿＿＿＿＿＿＿＿＿＿＿＿＿＿＿＿

2. Incident: ＿＿＿＿＿＿＿＿＿＿＿＿＿＿＿＿＿＿＿＿

＿＿＿＿＿＿＿＿＿＿＿＿＿＿＿＿＿＿＿＿＿＿＿＿＿＿

Feeling: ＿＿＿＿＿＿＿＿＿＿＿＿＿＿＿＿＿＿＿＿＿＿

＿＿＿＿＿＿＿＿＿＿＿＿＿＿＿＿＿＿＿＿＿＿＿＿＿＿

3. Incident: ＿＿＿＿＿＿＿＿＿＿＿＿＿＿＿＿＿＿＿＿

＿＿＿＿＿＿＿＿＿＿＿＿＿＿＿＿＿＿＿＿＿＿＿＿＿＿

Feeling: ＿＿＿＿＿＿＿＿＿＿＿＿＿＿＿＿＿＿＿＿＿＿

＿＿＿＿＿＿＿＿＿＿＿＿＿＿＿＿＿＿＿＿＿＿＿＿＿＿

4. Incident: _____

_____

Feeling: _____

_____

5. Incident: _____

_____

Feeling: _____

_____

If you are in a similar situation in the future, it is important to know that you have options in responding. In Column IV on your *Adult Inventory II*, you listed how you responded initially to each incident. As mentioned earlier, Column V gives you an opportunity to brainstorm alternative ways of behavior if in a similar situation. Though you have already listed one alternative, go ahead and list several more for each incident. This provides you with the freedom of several options as opposed to the restraints of only one solution.

Incident One: Options for future, similar situation.

a. _____
b. _____
c. _____

Incident Two: Options for future, similar situation.

a. _____
b. _____
c. _____

Incident Three: Options for future, similar situation.

a. _____
b. _____
c. _____

Incident Four: Options for future, similar situation.

a. _____
b. _____
c. _____

Action

Return to Column VI on both Inventories. It is now time to determine what action is necessary for resolving the unfinished business for each incident.

Anger

Perhaps it will be necessary to do *anger* work by:

- Smashing old plates in the garage.
- Beating the bed with a bat or tennis racket.
- Throwing balls of clay at the refrigerator.
- Stomping on empty soda cans.
- Pounding nails into a board with a hammer.
- Tearing up paper.
- Screaming while visualizing the person you are angry at.

Grief

Grief work might involve:

- Saying goodbye to a lost relationship in a letter.
- Having a funeral for the lost relationship or the death of a loved one.
- Crying while visualizing hugging yourself at the age of abuse.
- Visualizing saying goodbye to the parent who never was.
- Visualizing turning yourself, your inner child, parents, relationships, etc., over to your concept of a Higher Power.
- Writing a letter about your sadness to your inner child with your dominant hand, and then allowing the child within to write back to you with your non-dominant hand.

Letter Writing

You may need to *write letters:*

- To yourself, a self-forgiveness letter.
- To your parents.
- To others who have hurt you.
- To your spouse, lover, boss, friends or children.

List what action you are willing to take for each incident listed on your *Learning Years Inventory* and *Adult II Inventory*.

Action To Be Taken:

1. Incident: _____
   Action: _____
2. Incident: _____
   Action: _____
3. Incident: _____
   Action: _____
4. Incident: _____
   Action: _____

Remember, you have all the time in the world to complete your action step, but it might be important to prioritize these steps for yourself so you don't feel so overwhelmed.

Action 1: _____
Action 2: _____
Action 3: _____
Action 4: _____

Congratulations!
You Have Made It Through The Learning Years.

Take A Break!

CHAPTER

The Exploring Years
10-15

M any changes occur during The Exploring Years, not only emotionally and developmentally, but also physically. During the years of prepuberty and puberty, more commonly called pre-adolescence and adolescence, family stability is very important.

At this time, hormonally the body begins to change. This is accompanied by mood swings, growing pains, body changes with the growth of pubic hair, menstruation for females and the active production of sperm for males. This is a lot of change to deal with at one time! Adolescents at these ages begin the process of separation and individuation. During this time self-exploration is so important. "Who am I? Why do I exist? What will I be when I grow into an adult? How do I survive in the world?" are just a few of the questions racing through a child's mind during these years.

For most, adolescence alone is a very scary time. When complicated by the dysfunction of addiction or trauma, adolescence becomes more complex. When I was 13, my mother developed cancer. She covered up her fear of death with alcohol and pills. Her cancer was severe, but, though death was a strong possibility, it was never discussed. In adolescence I had a lot of confusion about death and wanted to talk about it, but the "no-talk rule" kept death a scary secret, not to be resolved until after my recovery.

Adolescents begin to want to break away from the family, but need to know as they did in earlier years that it is always possible to return to the safety the family provides when the world seems unsure. The phrase "growing up is hard to do" is especially apt during these years. With proper attention, nurturing, limit-setting and guidance, the road through adolescence is made easier. When there is addiction, rigidity, abandonment, rejection, little recognition and little attention, adolescence becomes a scary and lonely experience.

Let's take a look at your Exploring Years. By now you may be an old hand at the inventory process, but remember you can always refer to previous inventories if you get confused.

SURVIVAL SKILLS — THE EXPLORING YEARS 10-15

I.	II.	III.	IV.	V.	VI.
Hurt, resentment — person, place, time. (Facts only)	How I felt about it then.	How I feel about it now. (Unfinished business)	What I did in response to the situation. (Survival skills, co-dependent behavior)	What I would do today in a similar situation. (Recovery)	Action I need to take to heal from this experience. (Anger Work, Grief Work)

Now it is time to explore what similar present-day situations may be causing us concern. During my Exploring Years, my parents divorced. For years I never really understood why they divorced. I remember trying to "fix" their relationship, hoping they would agree to live together again. I desperately wanted a mother and a father living under the same roof, providing me with the parenting I saw my friends receiving from both of their parents.

In adulthood, I became a regular relationship busybody. No matter how hard I tried to avoid it, I seemed to constantly be triangulated or the middle person carrying messages between two in disagreement. When the relationships didn't work out, I was either blamed by the two parties involved or I felt as if I had in some way failed.

I was re-enacting my past attempts to repair my parents' relationship by allowing myself to be pulled into present-day relationships. By examining this, I was able to begin avoiding triangles in adulthood.

Let's take a look at any present-day resentments which might have patterns similar to those developed between the ages of 10 and 15.

SURVIVAL SKILLS INVENTORY — ADULT II

I.	II.	III.	IV.	V.	VI.
Hurt, resentment — person, place, time. (Facts only)	How I felt about it then.	How I feel about it now. (Unfinished business)	What I did in response to the situation. (Survival skills, co-dependent behavior)	What I would do today in a similar situation. (Recovery)	Action I need to take to heal from this experience. (Anger Work, Grief Work)

1. List the patterns you can identify in both inventories.
   a. Pattern: _____

   _____

   _____

   Survival Skill or purpose of behavior: _____

   _____

   _____

   b. Pattern: _____

   _____

   _____

   Survival Skill or purpose of behavior: _____

   _____

   _____

   c. Pattern: _____

   _____

   _____

   Survival Skill or purpose of behavior: _____

   _____

   _____

   d. Pattern: _____

   _____

   _____

   Survival Skill or purpose of behavior: _____

   _____

   _____

Find some pictures of yourself which correspond to your Exploring Years. Spend some time looking through them and journal any thoughts, feelings or memories you have of these times.

"When I look at pictures of myself between the ages of 10 and 15, I feel, remember or think of:" _____

_____

_____

You may begin having dreams about yourself at these ages or about children age 10 to 15. Remember that when we dream about other children, we are usually dreaming about ourselves. Journal any dreams you have had about this age period.

_____

_____

_____

_____

Let's examine the survival skills which were developed for our protection between the ages of 10 and 15. Look back over the list work you did on your *Exploring Years Inventory* and *Adult III Inventory*. Look for any similarities and list the survival skills you can identify in both inventories.

Survival Skills

My Survival Skills That Originated From Ages 10 To 15

1. _____
2. _____
3. _____
4. _____

How I Feel About Each Survival Skill (numb, sad, angry, confused)

1. _____
2. _____
3. _____
4. _____

How Does Each Survival Skill Cause Unmanageability
Or Problems In My Life Today?

1. _____
2. _____
3. _____
4. _____

How Have I Tried To Control, Alter, Ignore, Fix Or Minimize Each Of My Survival Skills?

1. _____
2. _____
3. _____
4. _____

What Is My Payoff For These Survival Skills?

1. _____
2. _____
3. _____
4. _____

What Price Or Losses Are My Survival Skills Costing Me Today In The Here And Now? (Loss of Self-Confidence, Self-Esteem, Financial, Emotional, Social)

1. _____
2. _____
3. _____
4. _____

How Did My Survival Skills Protect Me While Growing Up In My Family?

1. _____
2. _____
3. _____
4. _____

What Payoffs Or Gifts Did I Receive For My Survival Skills While Growing Up?

1. _____
2. _____
3. _____
4. _____

Unfinished Business

Look at your *Exploring Years Inventory Column III* titled Unfinished Business. List the unfinished business or feelings you continue to carry regarding your family history.
(Feelings: rage, shame, grief, loneliness, fear, numbness)

1. _____

2. _____

3. _____

4. _____

List the incident each feeling is related to on your Inventory and then list any other unfinished business which evokes this feeling for you.

1. Incident: _____

_____

_____

• Other unfinished business evoking this feeling: _____

_____

_____

2. Incident: _____

_____

_____

• Other unfinished business evoking this feeling: _____

_____

_____

3. Incident: _____

_____

_____

• Other unfinished business evoking this feeling: _____

_____

_____

4. Incident: _____

_____

_____

• Other unfinished business evoking this feeling: _____

_____

_____

Now let's look at any *Unfinished Business* we have in Column III of our *Adult III Inventory*. Write out all of your unfinished business, incident by incident, with the feelings corresponding to each situation below.

1. Incident: _____
   Feelings: _____
2. Incident: _____
   Feelings: _____
3. Incident: _____
   Feelings: _____
4. Incident: _____
   Feelings: _____

Now let's look at options for responding to similar situations in the future. Column IV on your *Adult Inventory III* lists how you responded to past situations. In Column V you were given an opportunity to list alternative ways of behaving in a situation similar to this in the future. Though you have listed one alternative, let's list several more for each incident in order to leave a variety of options for the future.

Incident One: Options for future, similar situation.

a. _____
b. _____
c. _____

Incident Two: Options for future, similar situation.

a. _____
b. _____
c. _____

Incident Three: Options for future, similar situation.

    a. _____

    b. _____

    c. _____

Incident Four: Options for future, similar situation.

    a. _____

    b. _____

    c. _____

Return to Column VI on both Inventories. Let's look at what action we must take in order to heal from these resentments and past experiences.

Do you need to do:

- Rage work
- Grief work
- Letter-writing
- Direct confrontation
- More visualizing of the incident in order to grieve or have your anger
- All of the above
- _____

(List anything else you feel would be appropriate.)

Action To Be Taken:

List what course of action you are willing to take for each incident listed on your *Exploring Years* and *Adult III Inventory*.

  1. Incident: _____

     Action: _____

  2. Incident: _____

     Action: _____

  3. Incident: _____

     Action: _____

  4. Incident: _____

     Action: _____

Remember once again that you can take as long as necessary to work through each action step. The only time limit will be the one you set for yourself. Let's prioritize our action steps.

- 1st action step to be taken: _____
- 2nd action step to be taken: _____
- 3rd action step to be taken: _____
- 4th action step to be taken: _____
- 5th action step to be taken: _____
- 6th action step to be taken: _____
- 7th action step to be taken: _____
- 8th action step to be taken: _____

Hurrah! Celebrate Your Honesty In Reviewing Your Exploring Years And Take A Break!

CHAPTER 8

More Growing Years

More Growing Years, 15-20

When I was between the ages of 15 and 20, my mother and my grandparents on my mother's side died. As my mother's life slowly came to an end from cancer, the discussion of her imminent death was avoided. At 16 I knew something didn't feel right, but I could never put my finger on it. When she did finally die, her death and the topic of death continued to be sidestepped.

As a consequence of this, I never really grieved the death of my mother and was even in denial of her passing until I reached recovery several years later. The denial about the death process was so incredible on my mother's side of the family that when my grandparents died a few years later, there weren't any funerals or memorials acknowledging their deaths.

These experiences left me with issues regarding death and the dying process. I couldn't go into a hospital for quite some time, and I refused to confront my own mortality. When close friends or relatives died, I had difficulty grieving for them. By re-examining how death was dealt with in my family system, I was able to heal from the loss of my mother and grandparents. By feeling the feelings of abandonment which are a consequence of such loss, I was also able to learn how to grieve those losses I had experienced in adulthood. I was then able to confront my own aging issues and make peace with my mortality.

Between the ages of 15 and 20, the steps toward adulthood begin to appear. It's an exciting time, but it also can be an unsure time. "Who am I? What is life really all about? Can I survive on my own?" and "What do I really want to do with my life?" continue to be questions in need of answers.

Questions about life, death, love, success, aging and security begin to produce direction in the life of a young adult. When the family system is dysfunctional, the adults in the system usually have not come to terms with the above issues themselves. As a consequence of this, it is difficult if not impossible for them to provide their offspring the necessary tools for addressing such issues.

The inability to confront these questions is carried on into adulthood, and this can affect us all of our lives. In the final section of our 4th Step, it is time to examine how those experiences between the ages of 15 and 20 continue to affect us today.

List any old resentments, traumas or pain which occurred between the ages of 15 and 20.

SURVIVAL SKILLS — MORE GROWING YEARS 15-20

I.	II.	III.	IV.	V.	VI.
Hurt, resentment — person, place, time. (Facts only)	How I felt about it then.	How I feel about it now. (Unfinished business)	What I did in response to the situation. (Survival skills, co-dependent behavior)	What I would do today in a similar situation. (Recovery)	Action I need to take to heal from this experience. (Anger Work, Grief Work)

By now you know the routine. It's time to examine what similar present-day situations are causing us concern. The unresolved issues surrounding the deaths of my mother and grandparents made it impossible for me not to over-react when a relationship came to an end or changed in any way. My deep-seated abandonment feelings about my childhood losses would be triggered whenever I experienced loss as an adult.

I had difficulty separating out my feelings and would eventually discover that my reactions were extreme for the situations being experienced in the here and now. Because of my unresolved loss, I not only felt my adult grief in present-day situations, but unknowingly felt my feelings about my childhood losses at the same time.

By comparing my reactions to adult loss with my experiences with childhood loss, it was easy to see that as an adult I reacted based on past experience. Today when I experience a loss, I can grieve *that* loss fully instead of complicating it with the feelings of past losses.

Let's see what current resentments, trauma or pain you have in the here and now which are similar in pattern to your experiences between the ages of 15 and 20.

SURVIVAL SKILLS — ADULT INVENTORY IV

I.	II.	III.	IV.	V.	VI.
Hurt, resentment — person, place, time. (Facts only)	How I felt about it then.	How I feel about it now. (Unfinished business)	What I did in response to the situation. (Survival skills, co-dependent behavior)	What I would do today in a similar situation. (Recovery)	Action I need to take to heal from this experience. (Anger Work, Grief Work)

1. List the patterns you can identify in both inventories.

   a. Pattern: _____

       _____

       _____

       Survival skill or purpose of behavior: _____

       _____

       _____

   b. Pattern: _____

       _____

       _____

       Survival skill or purpose of behavior: _____

       _____

       _____

   c. Pattern: _____

       _____

       _____

       Survival skill or purpose of behavior: _____

       _____

       _____

Look at some photos of yourself from ages 15 to 20 and record any feelings, memories or thoughts you might have.

_____

_____

_____

_____

If you begin to have dreams of yourself or other teenagers at these ages, it is important for you to journal them. They may contain important clues for your healing and recovery.

_____

_____

_____

Let's take a look at the survival skills you developed between the ages of 15 and 20. See if there are similarities in behavior you can identify on your *More Growing Years Inventory* and *Adult Inventory IV.*

Survival Skills

My Survival Skills Which Originated From Ages 15 to 20

1. _____
2._____
3. _____
4. _____

How I Feel About Each Survival Skill
(numb, sad, angry, confused)

1. _____
2._____
3. _____
4. _____

How Does Each Survival Skill Cause Unmanageability Or Problems In My Life Today?

1. _____
2._____
3. _____
4. _____

How Have I Tried To Control, Alter, Ignore, Fix Or Minimize Each Of My Survival Skills?

1. _____
2._____
3. _____
4. _____

What Is My Payoff For These Survival Skills?

1. _____
2. _____
3. _____
4. _____

What Price Or Losses Are My Survival Skills Costing Me Today In The Here And Now?
(Loss of self-confidence, self-esteem, financial, emotional, social)

1. _____
2. _____
3. _____
4. _____

How Did My Survival Skills Protect Me While Growing Up In My Family?

1. _____
2. _____
3. _____
4. _____

What Payoffs Or Gifts Did I Receive From My Survival Skills While Growing Up?

1. _____
2. _____
3. _____
4. _____

Unfinished Business

Now let's take a look at what unfinished business is listed in your *More Growing Years Inventory*, Column III (Feelings: rage, shame, grief, loneliness, fear, numbness)

1. _____

2. _____

3. _____

4. _____

List the incident each feeling is related to on your Inventory and then list any other unfinished business which evokes this feeling for you.

1. Incident: _____

_____

_____

   • Other unfinished business evoking this feeling: _____

_____

_____

2. Incident: _____

_____

_____

   • Other unfinished business evoking this feeling: _____

_____

_____

3. Incident: _____

_____

_____

   • Other unfinished business evoking this feeling: _____

_____

_____

4. Incident: _____

_____

_____

   • Other unfinished business evoking this feeling: _____

_____

_____

Now list the *Unfinished Business* you have under Column III of your *Adult Inventory IV*. List each feeling with its corresponding incident.

1. Incident: _____
   Feelings: _____
2. Incident: _____
   Feelings: _____
3. Incident: _____
   Feelings: _____
4. Incident: _____
   Feelings: _____

Look under Column IV on your *Adult Inventory IV*. Here you have listed alternative ways of behaving if caught in a similar situation in the future. Let's list a few more just to be on the safe side.

Incident One: Options for future, similar situation.

a. _____
b. _____
c. _____

Incident Two: Options for future, similar situation.

a. _____
b. _____
c. _____

Incident Three: Options for future, similar situation.

a. _____
b. _____
c. _____

Incident Four: Options for future, similar situation.

a. _____
b. _____
c. _____

Return to Column VI on both *Inventories*. Let's determine what action must be taken in order to heal from these hurts, experiences and resentments.

Action To Be Taken:

List the action to be taken for each incident listed on your *More Growing Years* and *Adult IV Inventory*.

1. Incident: _____
   Action: _____
2. Incident: _____
   Action: _____
3. Incident: _____
   Action: _____
4. Incident: _____
   Action: _____

Let's simplify the above tasks by prioritizing them. By doing this we will feel less overwhelmed.

1st action step to be taken: _____

2nd action step to be taken: _____

3rd action step to be taken: _____

4th action step to be taken: _____

5th action step to be taken: _____

6th action step to be taken: _____

7th action step to be taken: _____

8th action step to be taken: _____

Believe It Or Not, You Have Completed This Inventory.

Go Play For A While!

CHAPTER

9

What To Do Now

Doing a 4th Step inventory involves taking a huge action step. After doing an inventory, most will feel a sense of freedom. It's a cleansing experience which allows us to dump onto paper some of the shame, rage and grief we have been carrying around for years. It's as if our feelings move through our body to our finger tips down the pencil and pen onto the paper. After such an experience some of you will wonder what it was you were so afraid of.

Others of you may still feel incomplete, heavy or in pain. *This too* is very *normal*. At such times it is important to have the support of your 12-Step group, sponsor, therapist, etc. Know that your feelings are healing and an important part of your recovery.

Several of you will have uncovered more questions about your past. Initially discovering there is more to "work on" can overwhelm us. If we understand that this information is essential for our healing, we won't feel quite as overwhelmed.

In doing the 5th Step, some people share their 4th Step with another immediately. Others take a break, rest and wait a while before sharing what they have uncovered with another. However you choose to work your 5th Step, know that what is most important is that you trust the person you are sharing with.

If you fear being shamed, lectured at or told you didn't do it right, make sure you find someone who won't respond to you in this manner. In doing a 5th Step it is important to find that friend, therapist, sponsor, clergy or recovering buddy who will not only support you, but validate your reality and what you have discovered about your history and yourself in your 4th Step.

The importance of doing a 4th and 5th Step lies in the fact that one is forced to confront honestly those issues which for so long were not discussed or were kept secret. This process also allows us to grow into healthy adults as we take responsibility for ourselves and our actions.

As long as I was unaware that my dysfunctional survival skills were a product of the creativity of a child's mind during the trauma, I couldn't take responsibility for my actions and make change. Discovering that my dysfunctional behaviors were a consequence of my need for survival during my youth set me free because then I knew the power of change was at hand.

I no longer felt helpless and out of control, like the child who grew up helpless in chaos. I could finally be an adult, grow up, take care of myself responsibly and choose to behave in ways that worked for me instead of against me.

It is frustrating to live with sick survival skills controlling us. We feel powerless and at a loss over our behavior, not knowing what it is we need to do to *change*. We continually look outside ourselves for the Big Fix, not knowing that the answers lie within. By completing this 4th Step Inventory, you have taken responsibility for yourself by honestly going within. Now change is possible.

I *congratulate* you for your *courage* to risk and grow, and wish you the best of healing on your path of self-discovery.

Take Care And Keep On Keeping On!

RESOURCES

Addicts And Family of Addicted
Al-Anon, Al-Anon Adult Children of
Alcoholics and
Alateen Family Groups
P.O. Box 862 Midtown Station
New York, NY 10018-086

Alcholics Anonymous
Box 459
Grand Central Station
New York, NY 10163

Adult Children of Alcoholics
6381 Hollywood Blvd., Suite 685
Hollywood, CA 90028

Cocaine Anonymous
P.O. Box 1367
Culver City, CA 90232

Cult Awareness Network
2421 W. Pratt Blvd., Suite 1173
Chicago, IL 60645

Drugs Anonymous
P.O. Box 473, Ansonia Station
New York, NY 10023

Nar-Anon
P.O. Box 2562
Palos Verdes, CA 90274

Nar-Anon Family Groups
350 5th Street, Suite 207
San Pedro, CA 90731

Pill-Anon Family Programs
P.O. Box 120, Gracie Station
New York, NY 10028

Pills Anonymous
P.O. Box 473, Ansonia Station
New York, NY 10023

Co-dependents Anonymous —
Central Office
P.O. Box 5508
Glendale, AZ 85312

National Association for Adult
Children of Alcoholics
31582 Coast Highway, Suite B
Laguna Beach, CA 92677

Workaholics Anonymous
75 Grasslands Road
Valhalla, NY 10595
(914) 235-6026

Families

Caregivers Support Groups —
Community Care Resources
(612) 642-4046 — Wilder Foundation

Divorce Anonymous
P.O. Box 5313
Chicago, IL 60680

Families Anonymous
P.O. Box 344
Torrance, CA 90501
(P.O. Box 528, Van Nuys, CA 91409)

Parental Stress Service, Inc.
154 Santa Clara Ave.
Oakland, CA 95610

Parents Anonymous
22330 Hawthorne Blvd.
Torrance, CA 90503

Parents Without Partners
7910 Woodmont Ave.
Washington, DC 20014

Family Violence
Batterers Anonymous
P.O. Box 29
Redlands, CA 92373

Survivors Network
18653 Ventura Blvd., #143
Tarzana, CA 91356

Eating Disorders

Overeaters Anonymous
4025 Spenser Street, Suite 203
Torrance, CA 90503

Food Addicts Anonymous
P.O. Box 057394
West Palm Beach, FL 33405

Sexual Disorders

Sexual Addicts Anonymous
P.O. Box 3038
Minneapolis, MN 55414

CoSA (Co-dependents of Sexual Addicts)
Twin Cities CoSA
P.O. Box 14537
Minneapolis, MN 55414

Incest

Incest Survivors Anonymous
P.O. Box 5613
Long Beach, CA 90805

Sexual Abuse Anonymous
P.O. Box 80085
Minneapolis, MN 55408

Survivors of Incest Anonymous
P.O. Box 21817
Baltimore, MD 21222

Micellaneous Self-Help Information

Obsessive Compulsive Anonymous
P.O. Box 215
New Hyde Park, NY 11040

Phobics Anonymous
P.O. Box 1180
Palm Springs, CA 92263

Self-Help Center
1600 Dodge Ave.
Evanston, IL 60201